First published in the UK by HarperCollins Children's Books in 2009
1 3 5 7 9 10 8 6 4 2
ISBN: 978-0-00-731498-0
A CIP Catalogue record for this title is available from the British Library.
No part of this publication may be reproduced, stored in a retrieval system or transmitted in any form or
by any means, electronic, mechanical, photocopying, recording or otherwise, without the prior permission of
HarperCollins Publishers Ltd, 77-85 Fulham Palace Road, Hammersmith, London W6 8JB

www.harpercollins.co.uk

The *Me to You* oval, *Tatty Teddy* signature and Bear logo are all registered
Trade Marks of Carte Blanche Greetings Ltd. © Carte Blanche Greetings Ltd
® PO Box 500, Chichester, PO20 2XZ, UK

www.carteblanchegreetings.com

Printed and bound in Italy by L.E.G.O. Spa

Special Sister

You will always
find a friend
in a sister

Sisters remind us
of the fun we have
as children

The bond between sisters is unbreakable

WHEN friends don't
understand,
a sister will

Time spent with a sister
is so special

Through good times and bad,
a sister can always
be relied upon

Sisters are the best
listeners in the world

Sisters can speak to
each other without
saying a word

Having a sister means
knowing someone
will always be there

Sisters share future dreams
and past memories

A loving sister
is a special gift